The Ultimate Guide
to the Magical World

Written by Barbara Bazaldua,
Hannah Dolan, and Beth Landis Hester

Contents

Can You Spot a Fairy?

When the sun is shining and all of nature seems aglow, you can be sure the fairies are at work all around you!

Fairies are smaller than your hand - too tiny for most people to notice, and too quick for most grown-ups to see.

If you are very patient and very lucky, you may even hear the tinkling of bells as a fairy says hello.

It's best to look for fairies in dry weather - they almost never go out in the rain, because they cannot fly with wet wings.

Fairies try to hide from human sight, but you can find traces all around: a perfect flower, a gleam of coloured light, leaves lined up in a row, a faint scent of cinnamon ...

Fairies love shiny things like pebbles and mirrors, and tasty treats such as muffins and bread. Put these gifts outside your door, and a fairy may come near!

If you want to know lots more about fairies, just turn the page and see! This book is filled with fairy friends and stories about their hidden pixie world far away in Never Land ... and right outside your door ...

Arrival Day

When a baby laughs for the very first time, a fairy's life begins. The breeze carries her to Pixie Hollow, where she'll find her wings, her talent and a home full of enchantment. From the beginning, the new fairy is surrounded by welcoming friends. It's the start of a magical life!

Carried on the breeze to Never Land, a baby's first laugh takes flight on a petal or seed, like this fluffy wisp of dandelion.

Fairy wings are unique – just like a fingerprint.

Tink's arrival dress is made from soft dandelion fluff.

A Touch of Pixie Dust

The dandelion seed arrives at the Pixie Dust Tree, shimmering with possibility. It is then brought to life by a shower of pixie dust. The glittery substance changes this tiny piece of nature into fairy form.

A Fairy's Wings

Queen Clarion, the ruler of Pixie Hollow, greets all new arrivals. She helps them stretch out their wings and shows them how to use them. To Tinker Bell, everything is so new – but with the gentle queen as her guide, she is excited to learn!

Eager Audience

Fairies of every talent gather round to see the new fairy come into being and welcome her to Pixie Hollow. Watching from the branches of the Pixie Dust Tree, everyone wonders: What kind of fairy will she be?

First Flight

With pixie dust to help, Tinker Bell is ready to fly! She spreads her delicate wings wide, then holds Queen Clarion's hand for her very first flight. Tink is timid at first, but then she lets go and soars overhead.

Queen Clarion's golden gown and wings glow with pixie dust.

Nature fairies give each spring bloom a colourful coat of fairy paint.

Minister of Spring

Springtime Square's sparrow man-in-charge makes sure that every detail is in place before the Everblossom blooms. He then proudly leads the nature fairies to the Mainland to unveil their colourful work.

Welcome to Spring!

It is my honour to welcome you to this lovely season. The nature fairies have been hard at work painting every petal and bumblebee, and the baby birds are ready to hatch … I think you'll agree we're all ready to go. I only hope Queen Clarion approves!

It takes about 15 minutes to get the spots just right on a ladybird.

Garden fairies coax baby sproutlings into the soil, where they take root and grow.

Spring has Sprung

The fairies do their best to make each new spring prettier than the last. Every detail is carefully attended to, from the tiniest bugs to the most spectacular blossoms.

When the Everblossom blooms, it is time to take spring to the Mainland.

Fairy Talent
Tinker

Home
A teapot house

Favourite Pastime
Creating new inventions using "lost things" from the Mainland.

Tinker Bell

Feisty Tinker Bell is always on the lookout for her next adventure. This flitterific fairy often creates chaos, but only because she sees things differently from others. Tink is full of ideas and, even if she doesn't always succeed at something, she never gives up.

Tinker Bell is an independent fairy, but she knows that everyone needs a helping hand sometimes.

Tinker Talent

Tink is downhearted when she discovers that her fairy talent is being a tinker. She doesn't want to be a pots-and-pans fairy! But Tink soon realises that tinkering is so much more than that.

Fairy Friends

Tink's closest friends, Iridessa, Fawn, Silvermist and Rosetta, all have different talents and personalities, but they are there for each other – even when Tinker Bell gets herself into scrapes!

"There's got to be more to my life than just pots and kettles."

Tink wears her hair in a bun to keep it out of her way – especially when she's tinkering.

Rare Talent

Tinker Bell has a very strong talent. Queen Clarion has never known a tinker as talented as Tink.

Tink is only 12.5cm (5 inches) tall. No wonder she had to shorten her leaf dress!

Passionate Pixie

Tinker Bell acts on her emotions and often looks before she leaps – something that can cause her to run into problems! But the great thing about quick-thinking Tink is she always finds a way to fix them.

Nothing to Fear

Tinker Bell throws herself into everything, even if she might be scared at first. When she meets Lizzy, her fear soon disappears as she realises they are quite alike: they even both love the colour green!

Talent Symbol
A gleaming water bubble

Favourite Places
Lilypad Pond and
the babbling brook

Treasured Possession
A perfume mister filled
with water

Silvermist

Silvermist is as calming and soothing as the
water she loves. The bubbly water-talent fairy
has an upbeat attitude to life, and she is
always ready to listen to and help her friends.
Just being near her is naturally cheering!

Silvermist is very
sensitive to others'
moods, making her an
understanding friend.

Water Whisperer

As a water-talent fairy,
Silvermist can make waves
and ripples in water, string
delicate dewdrops on spider
webs – and she can even
understand babbling brooks!

"You've heard of the dewdrop.
This is a don't drop!"

Tender Teacher

Positive-thinking Silvermist
is an encouraging teacher.
"You can do it!" she tells Tinker
Bell. Even when Tink's water-talent
lesson ends in a splashy disaster,
Silvermist keeps her cool.

Pixie Peacekeeper

A "go-with-the-flow" kind of fairy, Silvermist is easily influenced by her friends, and she often changes her mind depending on what they say. This might seem a little wishy-washy, but Sil just hates to argue, so she tries to agree with everyone!

Silvermist wears her hair loose and flowing like a gentle stream.

Sensitive Sil
Water-talent fairies like Silvermist are very tender-hearted and can often cry easily.

This delicate gown is inspired by calla lily petals, Silvermist's favourite flower.

These dainty blue and silver slippers sparkle like water.

Iridessa

Warm-hearted Iridessa sees the inner light in her friends and loves to see them shine. Although she tries to look on the bright side, this realistic pixie knows things can go wrong faster than she can say "pixie dust", so Iridessa is always prepared!

Talent
Light Fairy

Home
A sunflower

Pet Peeves
Breaking the rules and not knowing the right answer

In every season, if something in nature gleams or glimmers, sparkles, shines or shimmers, there's a chance that Iridessa has helped create it.

Firefly Friends

Fireflies love Iridessa. When she whistles for them, they fly to her like eager puppies. She gathers light in her hands and throws it up in the air. The bugs then dart through the light and illuminate their plump little behinds.

Fairy Wings
Fairies' wings express their moods. When Iridessa is worried or upset, her wings sometimes droop.

Iridessa likes everything controlled and tidy – even her hair!

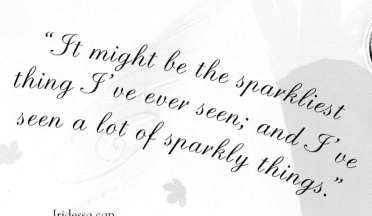

"It might be the sparkliest thing I've ever seen; and I've seen a lot of sparkly things."

Iridessa can catch light rays in her hands.

A sunflower seed makes a perfect brooch.

Iridessa gleams in her sunflower petal dress.

Carefully Does It

It's not easy to convince careful Iridessa to go along with spur-of-the-moment schemes – despite her friends' best efforts! But once she agrees, Iridessa puts her heart and soul into everything she does.

Practical Pixie

An organised "neatnik", Iridessa loves order. When she stores rainbows in tubes to take to the Mainland, she places them in a perfect pile.

Sky Artist

To make a rainbow, light- and water-talent fairies have to work together. As Silvermist throws mist into the air, Iridessa flies through it, painting a ribbon of colours across the sky. Beautiful!

Winter

Only winter fairies can fly in this realm. Everything here is freezing cold – even the Hall of Winter, where Pixie Hollow history is written on tablets of ice.

Autumn

In the Autumn Woods, the air is crisp, the leaves are kissed with gold and fairies are busy mixing the perfect colours for a spectacular autumn display.

Pixie Hollow

In Pixie Hollow, changing the seasons is as easy as flying from Springtime Square to the Autumn Woods! With all the seasons side by side, it's just the place for nature fairies to practise their talents. Right in the centre of it all is the magical Pixie Dust Tree, whose roots spread to every corner of the hollow.

Spring

A burst of colour and birdsong marks the spot where springtime lives. Here, pixies train plants to grow and flower, and help baby animals wake from their winter naps.

Summer

Lush and green, summer is a sight to behold! It is here that the fairies practise making sure every tree, stream, and animal is ready to dazzle on the Mainland.

A Fairy Paradise

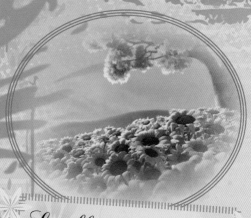

In the land of Pixie Hollow, where pixies live and play, there are all sorts of special places to explore – lively swimming holes, soothing meadows and pretty pathways that link it all up. Come take a stroll to get a close-up look … or grab some pixie dust and fly high to see it all!

Sunflower Meadow

The rich sunlight over Sunflower Meadow is a treasure for light fairies. Iridessa helps to gather it up and share it with the fireflies who live among the blooms.

Havendish Stream

This brook has waterfalls, pools and sandy beaches. How far do its waters go? With the right boat, a fairy could travel up Havendish Stream all the way to the Mermaid Lagoon.

Butterfly Cove

Colour takes flight in Butterfly Cove! It is the home of the butterflies and a favourite hangout of the animal fairies, who love to paint these stunning insects.

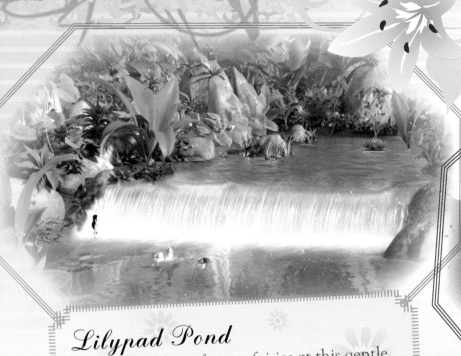

Lilypad Pond

You will find lots of water fairies at this gentle stream with a sparkling waterfall. When the fairies add soft ripples to the water's surface, this relaxing spot becomes extra magical.

Flower Garden

Blossoms of every kind bloom in Pixie Hollow, and the Flower Garden contains almost all of them. It takes the care of a garden fairy and a light fairy's touch of sun to help the flowers here look their best.

Springtime Square

This is the busy centre of the spring world. Piles of berries and seeds are all around and the paths are paved with flowers. The Everblossom here signals the start of spring.

Pine Tree Grove

Fairies and sparrow men stand guard in these treetop watchtowers, looking out for hawks and other dangers. If they use their shell horns to sound a warning, it's time to take cover!

Regal Role

Rules Pixie Hollow

Home

Royal rooms in the
Pixie Dust Tree

Pet Peeves

Squabbling fairies
and hurricanes

Queen Clarion

Meet the most beautiful and powerful fairy in all of Pixie Hollow – Queen Clarion. The graceful queen rules Pixie Hollow with kindness, humour and wisdom. In return, all the fairies love, respect and trust her to always make the right decision.

"Born of laughter, clothed in cheer, happiness has brought you here."

Welcoming Tinker Bell to Pixie Hollow, Queen Clarion gently spreads out Tink's wings and teaches her to fly.

Fair but Firm

Although she is always calm and patient, Queen Clarion sometimes needs to be firm with her fairies. She especially dislikes bickering or mean-spiritedness – and she makes sure that her subjects know about it!

Hall of Sceptres

Queen Clarion lives in the Pixie Dust Tree. It has many beautiful rooms, from the elegant throne room where she meets her ministers, to the shining Hall of Sceptres.

Wings are larger and more magnificent than any other fairy's.

Pixie Dust Queen

When Queen Clarion appears, she is first seen as sparkles of pixie dust dancing through the air. Then the pixie dust comes together in the shape of her shimmering form.

Timeless

Queen Clarion's arrival day was long ago, but her beauty stays bright because fairies don't age.

Queen Clarion always keeps her regal poise.

Guiding Light

Queen Clarion encourages her subjects to have the confidence to do things for themselves and learn from their mistakes – especially headstrong Tinker Bell! Queen Clarion is very fond of young Tink.

23

Talent Symbol

A paw print

Home

A treehouse carved from
a giant pinecone

Favourite Games

Leapfrog and
fairy tag

Fawn

One of Tinker Bell's closest friends, Fawn is an athletic animal fairy who spends her days helping and playing with animals. She loves all creatures, big or small! Fawn's easy-going attitude makes her a great friend to animals and pixies alike.

Animals adore Fawn. Her kind, understanding and caring manner makes every creature feel safe.

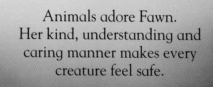

Mischief Maker

A good sport with a lively sense of humour, Fawn loves to play mischievous pranks on her friends. She is especially fond of teasing Rosetta and Iridessa – they're the easiest fairies to fool!

Soaring Salute

For the Autumn Revelry, Fawn prepares a special 21-butterfly salute. At her signal, the lovely creatures will soar into the sky. Ready, set – flutter!

A vine headband keeps Fawn's hair tidy.

No-Fuss Fairy

A rough-and-tumble tomboy, Fawn is happiest having adventures outdoors and prefers practical clothing to dainty dresses. Fawn's job often means she gets a little dirty and smelly (especially when she trains skunks!) but Fawn doesn't mind.

A long hair braid suits Fawn's active lifestyle.

Moss top is belted with green vine.

Fawn dresses for action in comfy leaf leggings.

"Easy, boy. It's all right. Fawn's got 'ya."

Critter Chatter
Animal fairies like Fawn can speak different animal languages. Fawn's favourite is "Toad".

Wake Up Sleepyhead

When Fawn helps bring spring to the Mainland, it's her job to awaken all the animals who have been hibernating. She even has their breakfast ready!

Fawn's practical boots are perfect for visiting animals on any terrain.

Talent Symbol

Flower

Home

A rose blossom

Favourite Pastime

Giving her friends
makeovers

Rosetta

There's a touch of the southern belle about
Rosetta. She's ladylike, genteel and very
well-mannered. But the ultra-feminine garden
fairy has a sharp, sassy wit and can be quite
outspoken – in the most charming way, of course!

Blossoms and buds,
vines and veggies,
fruits and friendships
grow with Rosetta's
dainty touch.

Looking Lovely

As pretty as her flowers,
Rosetta is very into
looks – especially her
own. She even has a
powder puff for applying
her pixie dust! She may
be a garden fairy, but
there is never a speck or
smudge of dirt on Rosetta.

Unlikely Friendship

Although Rosetta prefers
girly, pretty things and
Fawn has a love of mud and
spiders, the two fairies are
close friends. They are
different, but they both love
to nurture living things.

No hair is ever
out of place.

*"Don't get your
wings in a bunch."*

Sweet Talk

Rosetta's relationship with
growing beautiful blooms
and perfect plants shows
in the cute nicknames
she gives her friends, like
"sweet pea" and "sugarcane".

Rosetta is partial to
pink. It's so flattering!

Dainty sandals
show off her
tidy toes!

Artistic Types

*Naturally artistic, garden fairies
like Rosetta paint each
spring flower and autumn
leaf in glowing hues.*

Her frilly skirt
is made of
rose petals.

Always Busy

Rosetta is busy in every
season, either planting,
painting petals and
leaves, or ripening fruits
and vegetables. In
autumn, Rosetta gets
corn ready to be eaten.

Fairy Friendship

Tinker Bell's warm heart and fun sense of adventure has won her many friends, including Rosetta, Silvermist, Fawn, Iridessa and Vidia. They are all different, but they are the best of buddies. Tink's big ideas and quick temper can get her into scrapes sometimes, but her friends are there to give her love, support and lots of hugs through the good times and the bad.

Lost Things

Mysterious objects lie waiting to be discovered on the sandy shores of Never Land. Washed up from the Mainland are broken toys, loose screws, a bit of this and that...Could these lost human objects become found treasures for the fairies of Pixie Hollow?

If you look carefully, and the sun shines just right, the glint of treasure can be seen from high above.

Junk or Gems?

Fairy Mary would take one look at this cove and leave – she doesn't need that junk! But when Tinker Bell discovers it, she can't believe all the glistening treasures before her eyes. She can imagine so many ways to use each piece of scrap.

Shimmering jewel

Round beads

Spiky pin

Musical harmonica

Possibilities

Tinker Bell loves visiting the beach to see what's new and get inspired. Would that metal spring add some bounce to a bug-painting tool? Could that harmonica become a work table for a tinker? It's so much fun to explore!

Supply Shopping

Tinker Bell can't resist taking as many interesting lost things as she can carry back home to Tinkers' Nook. Even if she's not quite sure how to use them … yet!

Shiny coin

Metal spring

Twisting screw

Tinkling bell

Tink's Challenge

Some may see just a pile of junk, but Tinker Bell can spot something special in these bits and pieces. Can she fit them together to bring this music box back to life?

Every invention begins with a bright idea. Next comes careful planning: every spring, screw and thingie in its place!

Tink's Inventions

What's even more powerful than pixie dust? Imagination and hard work! That's how Tinker Bell changes her collection of lost things that she finds into amazing tools for fairies of every talent.

Spring

The Berry Crusher

With a gear and a spring found near Havendish Stream, Tinker Bell turned a nutcracker made from sticks and stones into a high-pressure berry crusher for making paint!

Gear

Tinkering Tink

Tinker Bell sees possibilities in every bit of "junk" she finds. She works hard to make each one something special and new. Her inventions might not always work, but that doesn't mean she stops trying!

Tweezers make a great grabbing tool.

a Glove whith the a pump

Squeeze-bulb from a perfume bottle.

The Seed Sower

Planting seeds takes the careful attention of several garden fairies – or one blast from Tink's automatic sower! Just squeeze the perfume-bottle bulb to suck seeds up into the glove's fingers, then let go and the burst of air shoots the seeds from the harmonica.

Gardening glove with holes in the fingertips.

Harmonica

The Spot Sprayer

What's a ladybird without its spots? Just a bug in need of this handy machine! Instead of dotting each one by hand, a fairy can paint a whole ladybird with a single pop from this speedy tool.

Paint pot

Turn this screw to release the spots!

Hollow vines

Tinker Bell is always focused when she is inventing something new!

Painted pussywillow puffs

Spinning wheel

Waiting customers

The Stripe Painter

Time to paint the bumblebees? It's easy with Tink's stripe-painting machine! With ink-tipped pussywillow puffs, this wheel spins to make perfect lines in seconds.

Tinker-made stone hammer.

The pointy nib of a fountain pen.

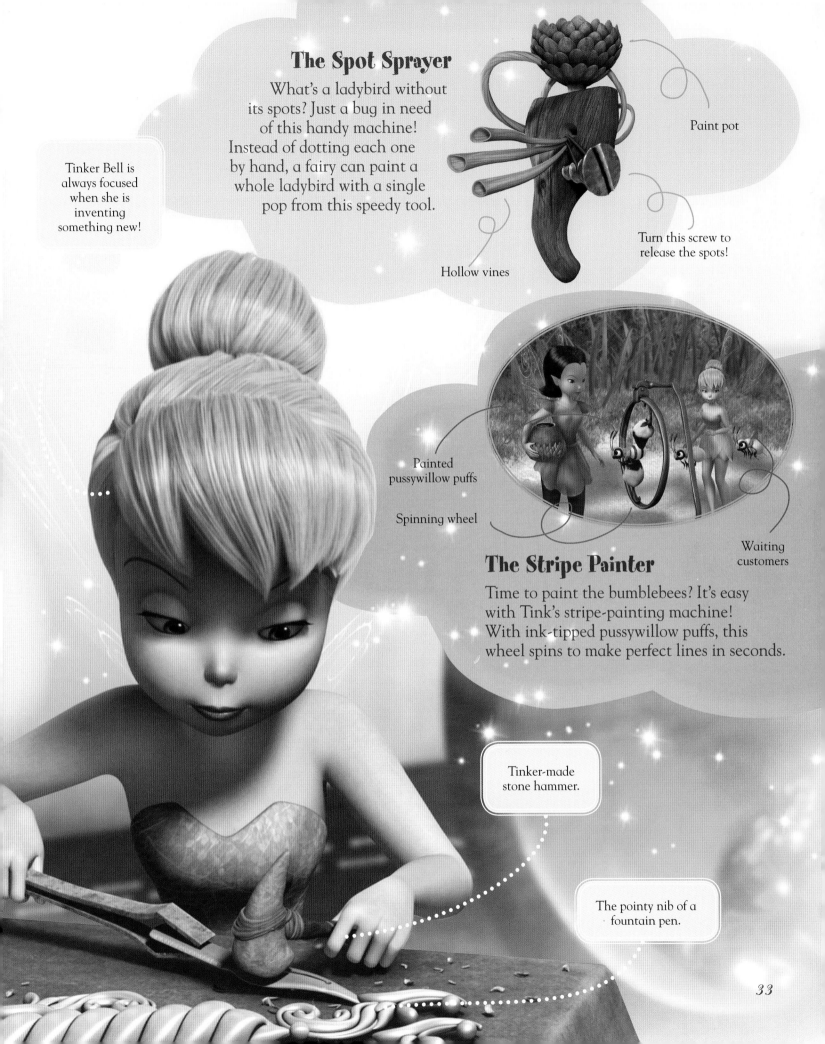

Vidia

Talent Symbol
Whirlwind

Home
A solitary sour plum tree at the edge of Pixie Hollow

Favourite Game
Racing dragonflies

Look out for Vidia! She's the fastest flying fairy in all of Pixie Hollow and a force of nature to be reckoned with. Vidia has intelligence, speed and courage, but her spiteful attitude stops most fairies from hanging around her long enough to see that she can be kind-hearted, too.

Teasing Tink

Boastful Vidia loves to tell everyone – especially Tink – just how special and rare her own talent is. The competitive sprite does all she can to make Tink feel bad about her skills.

Vidia's fast-flying talent is very strong, but so is Tink's tinkering talent – a fact that makes Vidia very jealous.

Embarrassing Moment

Barely escaping a dangerous hawk, Vidia ends up splattered with berry juice. Although they're glad she's okay, the other fairies can't help laughing. The proud pixie's attitude hasn't won her many friends in Pixie Hollow.

"*I make forces of nature.*"

Vidia likes to smirk and pout a lot, but she is prettiest when she smiles.

Vidia

Sleek pony tail keeps hair out of Vidia's eyes while flying.

Fit for Flight
Wet wings don't soar, so fast-flying fairies are extra careful to keep theirs completely dry.

Snidely Speaking

When Vidia calls other fairies "dear" and "sweetie", she is usually being sarcastic. But eventually Vidia learns the value of friendship, and she begins to really mean it!

Feathers give Vidia extra lift in the air.

Leggings are streamlined for faster flying.

High-flier

Vidia's fast-flying talent helps the other fairies create all the seasons. She makes whirlwinds to gather spring pollen and blustery winds for autumn leaves.

Fairy Houses

A fairy's home fits her in every way! Not only is it the perfect tiny size, but it suits her talent and personality, too. These magical houses are made from things found in nature, like leaves, twigs and shells, so humans might look right over them without even noticing!

Blossom Beds

Fairies rest where they feel most at home. Iridessa and other light fairies bed down in the silky-soft petals of sunflowers, while flower fairies, like Rosetta, make their homes within the blooms they care for.

The Sour Plum Tree

Vidia lives alone in this solitary, sour-fruited tree on the edge of a cliff. She hopes that other fairies will get the message: no visitors!

Mushroom steps lead up to the house.

The teapot-lid door swings open.

There is a hole in the teapot, so a leaf roof keeps the rain out.

An upturned shell makes a perfect flowerpot.

Tink's Teapot

Perched atop a tree root in Tinkers' Nook is Tinker Bell's teapot home. It is filled with tools, lost things and other useful materials … at least they *might* be useful, if she could just figure out a way to use them all!

Tinker Interiors

Tink's cottage is stocked with everything a tinker could need: a sturdy harmonica work table, a cosy petal bed and a wardrobe filled with leaf dresses.

37

Find Your Fairy Talent

When Tinker Bell arrives in Pixie Hollow, everyone gathers to watch her discover her talent. It's a very important part of the welcoming ceremony – finding your unique gift is a way of learning who you really are.

Talent Types

Fairies place glowing icons representing their talents on mushroom tables in front of Tinker Bell. Tink worries that she won't know which talent is hers, but Queen Clarion puts her at ease – she will just know.

First, Tink touches a glowing flower, but it fades and droops. She is not a garden-talent fairy.

When Tink touches a small stone hammer, golden lights bursts forth. Even the queen is amazed. Tink has a true talent for tinkering!

A tiny whirlwind disappears at Tink's touch. Vidia smiles scornfully – Tink is not a fast-flying fairy like her!

Silvermist nods encouragement as Tink touches a water drop, but it bursts. Water is not her talent either.

Fairy Talents

What's the perfect Pixie Hollow job for you? The answer is different for every fairy and sparrow man, but the key to finding it is the same: listen to your heart, find your talent and do your very best!

❀ **Type:** Garden-talent fairy

Tasks: Plant seeds and sproutlings and help plants and flowers grow

Hangout: Flower Garden

❀ **Type:** Dust-keeper fairy

Tasks: Give just the right amount of pixie dust to every fairy and sparrow man

Hangout: Pixie Dust Depot

❀ **Type:** Animal-talent fairy

Tasks: Teach birds to fly, help fuzzy creatures hibernate, be a helper to all animals

Hangout: Anywhere animals fly, crawl or swim!

❀ **Type:** Healing-talent fairy

Tasks: Fix up bumps and bruises on fairies who are wounded or treat fairies who are sick

Hangout: Fairy Urgent Care

※ **Type:** Light-talent fairy

Tasks: Gather sunbeams, train fireflies, guide sunlight onto flower petals and autumn leaves

Hangout: Sunflower Meadow

※ **Type:** Water-talent fairy

Tasks: Make ripples in ponds, put dewdrops on leaves and spiderwebs

Hangout: Lilypad Pond

※ **Type:** Fast-flying fairy

Tasks: Whirl up gentle breezes, gusts of wind and other forces of nature

Hangout: Flying in the skies over Pixie Hollow

※ **Type:** Tinker-talent fairy

Tasks: Make useful tools and vehicles to help fairies and sparrow men do their jobs

Hangout: Tinkers' Nook

※ **Type:** Frost fairy

Tasks: Makes frost swirls on leaves and plants

Hangout: The Winter Woods

Teaching Tink

When Tinker Bell learns that tinker fairies don't go to the Mainland, she decides to change her talent and talks her friends into teaching her how to do theirs. Tink's friends aren't so sure it'll work, but they all agree to give it a try!

Splash Alert!

Silvermist shows Tink how to decorate spider webs with water drops. Sil makes it look so easy, but Tink can't stop dropping the drops! When it comes to learning a water talent, Tink is all wet.

Light Lesson

Iridessa chooses a "simple" light talent task to teach Tink, but while trying to capture the sunset's golden rays to make fireflies glow, Tink lights up her own behind instead of theirs!

Bird Business

Tink sets out to teach a baby bird to fly following Fawn's instructions, but she's not used to talking to birds. Tink scares the bird so much that it tries to get back into its egg!

Prickly Disaster

When Tink asks Vidia how to be a fast-flying fairy, spiteful Vidia invents a task that Tink will fail – rounding up the impossible-to-catch sprinting thistles! It ends in disaster for the fairies' springtime preparations.

Talented Tinker

When Tink finds a broken music box, she just has to fix it. Tink soon realises that a tinker is who she is inside. In the end, she gets to return the music box to its owner – on the Mainland!

Clank

This tinker is big and strong, and he has a big heart, too. Boisterious Clank is a bit of a bumbler, but he is so cheerful that no one minds. He does everything with lots of energy and enthusiasm – even talking. He often interrupts his best buddy Bobble, or even finishes his sentences, which can drive Bobble crazy!

Talent
Tinker

Greatest Invention
Fireworks launcher

Pet Peeves
None. He's much too easy-going to get peeved!

Clank is fascinated by the lost things Tink finds – it's just a shame Fairy Mary isn't!

Clowning Around

Peek-a-boo! Clank loves acting silly and doing things to make others smile. Perhaps Clank would get more tinkering work done and stay out of trouble with Fairy Mary if he didn't spend so much time clowning around!

Clank plugs his delicate ears with cotton fluff while he is tinkering!

A cool and comfortable leaf tunic is Clank's favourite work wear.

"Haydee hi, haydee ho, Miss Bell!"

Sparrow Men
Male fairies of any talent are known as sparrow men, but it's okay to call them fairies, too.

Strong Sparrow Man

This tinker's big size (for a fairy) and strength can be very useful in his work as a tinker. He can lift up a cart that needs its wheel repairing as if it's cotton fluff – but he is just as likely to accidentally drop it!

Top Talent

Clank is proud of his tinker talent. He thinks of it as "real" work! Clank's feelings are hurt when Tink doesn't appreciate being a tinker at first but, together with Bobble, he does his best to show her that tinkers rock!

Real Name

Phineas T. Kettletree, Esq.

Talent

Tinker

Home

Shares a knothole bungalow in a treeroot with his best pal, Clank

Bobble

Tinkering is never boring, according to Bobble. This smart sparrow man is a tinkering enthusiast – he is the fairy to come to if you need to know a seven-gauge twig from a five-gauge! A loyal friend, Bobble is often in trouble with Fairy Mary for covering up for his friends.

Big-hearted Bobble and Clank are eager to make Tinker Bell feel at home when she arrives in Tinkers' Nook.

Bobble Goggles

Bobble's thick glasses make his eyes look big and bobbly. Maybe that's why he got his nickname. Bobble just puts a dewdrop in each lens, and he's ready for close-up tinkering!

Born to Tinker

Bobble loves inventing new gadgets and gizmos. He is a real tinker geek! Bobble is proud of his tinkering work and knows how important it is to everyone in Pixie Hollow.

Friendly Fairy

Bobble is thrilled to discover that his friend Tinker Bell has a tinkering talent like no other. Bobble can usually be found with Tink or his other best buddy, Clank. Bobble and Clank often argue, but they are good friends really!

Comfortable work pants made from moss.

Tinkers Rule
Bobble gets lots of practise at following an important tinker rule: Learn from your mistakes!

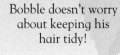

Bobble doesn't worry about keeping his hair tidy!

"We're pleased as a pile of perfectly polished pots you're here!"

Tool belt filled with tinkering tools.

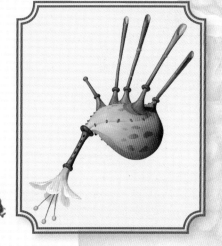

Hidden Talent

Bobble's most treasured possessions are his bagpipes – though many of the fairies wish they weren't! He made them himself from flowers and leaves.

How to be a Tinker

Are you our brand-new tinker?
Well, teetering teapots! We're delighted
to have you. Do you know how to make
a rainbow tube? Never mind – we'll tell
you everything you need to know.
Come into the workshop and we'll
show you what we tinkers do!

Not every project
seems exciting at
first, but stick with
it – even a teapot
is important to
somebody!

Toadstools make
comfortable work
stations

Rainbow tubes
for light fairies

Finished acorn teapot

Folded from soft leaves, tinkers
make saddles and satchels for
carrying anything a fairy
might need to the Mainland.

Pixie dust sacks

Flower spotlight,
lit by a firefly

Paintbrushes and pots
for art fairies

Much to Make

Clank and Bobble love to
share the things they've
made – like this mound of
pots, kettles, baskets and
bushels in the tinker storage
room – and to see how much
their work helps others.

Busy Fairies

Fairies from all over Pixie Hollow
come to tinker fairies for the tools
they need. In their busy workshop,
tinkers work on a whole bunch
of projects at the same time.
Every tinker fairy has their own
way of working: sitting on a stool,
pacing on the mossy floor or even
hovering in the air. Take your pick!

Acorn buckets
for supplies

Tinker Tools:

Stone hammer

Thorn scissors

Sticks

Soft leaves

Grass ties

Leaf notepad
(like this one!)

Role
Head tinker fairy

Relaxation Method
Counting slowly.
She once reached 1,493!

Favourite Pastime
Going to the
Fairy Tale Theatre

Fairy Mary

She might not have the most glamorous job in Pixie Hollow, but Fairy Mary knows how important her role as head tinker fairy is. She manages the tinker fairies and makes sure they have plenty of supplies. Tinkers' Nook would be in disarray were it not for this resourceful fairy!

A teacher as well as a tinker, Fairy Mary tells Tinker Bell to be true to herself. It's the only way to be happy.

Keeping Count
One-hundred acorn buckets, three-dozen baskets …Fairy Mary zips around the workshop, fingers flying over her abacus as she keeps her team's projects on track.

No Junk Allowed!
Keeping things neat is important to Fairy Mary, so when she sees Tink's lost things, she whisks them away. There should be no rubbish cluttering her workshop!

Hairdo is a
no-fuss bun.

"You are a tinker. It's who
you are. Be proud of it."

Happy Home
Tinker fairies don't go to
the Mainland, but Fairy
Mary doesn't mind. She's
happiest in her workshop.

When Fairy Mary has her
arms crossed, it can often
mean a tinker is about to
get a ticking off!

No Fooling Fairy Mary
Like the mother of mischievous
children, Fairy Mary knows when
someone (often Clank or Bobble)
is messing about. She's strict –
but the twinkle in her eye tells
her fairies she cares about them.

Leaf tunic and
trousers are cool
and practical
for work.

Bursting with Pride
Fairy Mary knows what an amazing
talent Tinker Bell has – although
she does feel the young fairy needs
to build up her tinkering muscles!
Fairy Mary thinks of Tink as her
personal prodigy and is proud
of her accomplishments.

Tinkers' Nook

This busy corner of Pixie Hollow is buzzing with activity. The tinker fairies live and work here, coming up with useful tools to help the other fairies. Under Fairy Mary's watchful eye, each clever creation is tested and perfected by the tinkers... eventually!

Tinkers work together in the workshop, at spacious toadstool tables lit by firefly lamps.

Each tinker has a little house.

A stream floats tools downstream.

A Tinker's Work

Tinkering means putting together bits and pieces to fix what's broken or make something new. Tinkers like Bobble and Clank can create all kinds of things from simple twigs, leaves and shells, like this delivery cart.

Special Delivery

The tinkers' inventions help fairies go about their work in every part of Pixie Hollow. It's up to Cheese the mouse to get them there in his tinker-made delivery cart.

Busy tinkers dart around, leaving trails of pixie dust.

Fairies use carts to move creations around the nook.

Flower pulley system picks up supplies.

Magical Nook

Located on the bare forest floor, in a twisted tangle of tree roots, Tinkers' Nook doesn't have the bright colours of some other parts of Pixie Hollow. But it is home to some very bright ideas!

The Queen's Review

Before springtime plants and animals are revealed on the Mainland, every detail is reviewed by Queen Clarion. In Springtime Square, the fairies and animals line up to show the queen what they have prepared. When the Everblossom blooms, it is time to take spring to the Mainland.

Helpful Role

A cheerful and friendly helping hand to the tinkers

Home

The barn in Tinkers' Nook

Pet Peeves

Loud noises and sprinting thistles

Cheese

A merry little field mouse, Cheese is not only an important helper to the fairies, he is also their beloved pet. The fairies named him Cheese because every time they yell "cheese", he always comes running!

Wherever the fairies go, Cheese goes, too. Cheese arrives in style for fairy camp, being flown in by a dove in his own little gourd.

Scaredy-Mouse

Cheese enjoys pulling the tinker fairies' supply cart, except for when he has to go through Needlepoint Meadow, where the speedy sprinting thistles hide. It's scary! Like all mice, Cheese can be timid, but he feels braver when Tink is around.

Mouse Talk

Watch the eyebrows! Cheese wiggles them to show his feelings.

These big soft ears hear tiny sounds that even fairies miss.

Cheese doesn't speak, but he communicates his thoughts and emotions clearly with his big eyes, twitching nose, whiskers, ears and funny little squeaks and chatters.

When Cheese is sad or nervous, his whiskers droop until they almost touch the ground.

Helping Paws
Fairies raise and train field mice, so Cheese has many squeaky friends and relations around him.

Giddy-up!
At first, Cheese is reluctant to help Tink catch some sprinting thistles, but he soon proves that he can run faster than a pony at a rodeo roundup. That mouse can move!

57

Garden fairies make a field of young pumpkins turn orange and ripe.

Animal-talent fairies guide tired geese to land after a long flight.

Autumn Hues

Nature seems to glow from within when fairies add an autumn touch. Pixies practise their craft all year round so it's perfect by autumn – right down to the littlest leaf!

Revelry

The fairies celebrate the end of autumn with the great Autumn Revelry. Every eight years, the revelry becomes extra special when the blue harvest moon rises. A sceptre is built to catch the moon's blue light, which creates powerful blue pixie dust.

Autumn leaves get a gorgeous amber glow.

Minister of Autumn

Kindly but cautious, the Minister of Autumn likes to listen to new ideas, but is happiest to stick to old traditions. He knows that the fairies will make the season beautiful, year after year.

Behold Autumn!

In the crisp autumn air, nature fairies do the noble work of gathering seeds, settling animals to hibernation and preparing all of nature to rest and regenerate. We welcome you to celebrate our traditions in this golden season!

Fairy Talent
Dust-keeper fairy

Home
The dust-keepers' dormitory, near the Pixie Dust Depot

Pet Peeve
Oversleeping – he likes to be up at the crack of dawn!

Terence

As a dust-keeper fairy, Terence helps make Pixie Hollow the magical place it is – but he is so modest that he doesn't think of himself that way! Easy-going Terence is the opposite of his fiery friend Tinker Bell, but he understands her better than anyone.

Terence's job involves giving each fairy a daily "dusting", and sprinkling dust on new fairies on their arrival day.

Firm Friends

Terence has taken Tinker Bell under his wing since she arrived in Pixie Hollow – even though his friends at the Pixie Dust Depot like to tease him about their close friendship!

Brave and Bold

Usually peace-loving, Terence can be very courageous – especially when it comes to helping Tinker Bell! He battles vicious rats to defend Tink and Blaze when they venture to the Lost Island.

An acorn cap makes a great beret.

Talented Terence

Hard-working Terence puts as much effort into his friendships as he does to his dust-keeping work. A friend to everyone, he is cheerful, helpful, and calm – even when Tink has one of her blow-ups. Now that takes talent!

The dust-keeper fairies wear brown and tan leaf uniforms.

A nutshell bag holds pixie dust deliveries for distant fairies.

"Hey . . . what are friends for?"

A Dusty Job

Fairies get a daily cupful of pixie dust, but dust-keepers don't need it – their work keeps them dusty all day.

Wrist bands give support while lifting heavy bags of pixie dust.

Dust Enthusiast

Terence loves his job as a dust-keeper fairy and has a passion for pixie dust. He sees himself as a "pixie dustologist"! When Tinker Bell needs some pixie dust advice, Terence is only too happy to help.

Slender leaf leggings allow freedom to move while working in the Pixie Dust Depot.

Fairy Gary

Big and burly Fairy Gary is head dust-keeper at the Pixie Dust Depot. A strict taskmaster, he is also fair and kind. Fairy Gary loves to tease and share a joke with his fairy workers – just as long as they don't mention his kilt!

Role

Head dust-keeper fairy

Pet Peeve

Rule-breaking

Treasured Possessions

Teacups – Fairy Gary has the largest collection in Pixie Hollow

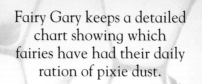

Fairy Gary keeps a detailed chart showing which fairies have had their daily ration of pixie dust.

Busy Boss

As head dust-keeper, Fairy Gary oversees every part of the pixie dust process. He loves order and efficiency, and it fills him with joy to see the Pixie Dust Depot running smoothly.

No Favourites

Responsible for making sure there's enough pixie dust to go around, Fairy Gary never bends the rules. No one gets extra – not even Tinker Bell.

"Remember, one cup each. No more, no less."

Daily Dust

Pixie dust is very precious in Pixie Hollow. Without Fairy Gary, every fairy would be grounded!

Brown leaf waistcoat and tan undershirt match Fairy Gary's comfortable kilt perfectly.

Kilt Concerns

When the other dust-keeper fairies tease Fairy Gary for wearing a "skirt", it bothers him. He talks about it to wise Mr Owl, whoo-whoo cheers him up!

Kilt is woven from brown and tan leaves, with a vine belt and white pebble fastener.

Leaf work boots are sturdy and practical.

Big Bear

With his growly Scottish accent, bushy eyebrows, tousled hair and thick whiskers, Fairy Gary resembles a huggable bear. No wonder Tinker Bell thinks he's so cute!

Pixie Dust

A sprinkle of shimmering pixie dust makes everything more magical! All fairies need their daily teacupful of dust in order to fly, and fairies of every talent use it in their work, too. Whether it's to give nature an enchanted glow, to make things float in the air or to oil a squeaky tinker-made machine.

Animal fairies use pixie dust to help furry creatures wake up from hibernation.

The Blue Moon

When the light of the blue moon passes through a special moonstone, it creates blue pixie dust that replenishes the fairies' supply of pixie dust. It's a special honour and a big challenge to make a sceptre for the moonstone. Does Tink have what it takes?

Anything can fly with a sprinkling of pixie dust, even a human's music box!

Pixie dust originates from the Pixie Dust Well inside the Pixie Dust Tree.

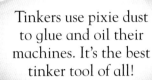

Tinkers use pixie dust to glue and oil their machines. It's the best tinker tool of all!

Garden fairies make leaves and flowers glow brighter with a touch of pixie dust.

Pixie Dust Depot

New pixie dust comes from the Pixie Dust Tree, but it is stored and distributed in the nearby Pixie Dust Depot. Fairy Gary and his team of dust-keepers measure out the right amount of pixie dust for every kind of fairy magic.

Dust-keeper fairies make sure each fairy gets one teacupful of pixie dust every day so they are able to fly.

Fairy Tale Theatre

Fairy Mary is a big fan of the theatre and never misses a show! Her special binoculars help her get even closer to the action.

Beneath this leaf-covered dome, the amazing true stories of the pixies' past are told. Just like in a human theatre, the audience gathers here to watch a show and have fun. But this is a fairy theatre – so you can be sure that every story has a magical twist!

Step Inside...

Nestled among mossy tree roots, this tinker-built dome was made especially for theatre. Inside, shows are performed above the audience within the tall ceiling space, so every seat is the best in the house!

> Door slides shut when the show begins.

Animal Orchestra

An animal-talent fairy conducts frogs, crickets and other critters to click, buzz and croak pretty music for the show. There are even crashing cymbals made from coins strapped to ladybirds' wings!

Golden light shines through the leaves, telling fairies that the show is about to start.

The audience watches the interactive theatre scenes from toadstool seats.

Story-tellers

Story-telling fairies like Lyria act out shows at the theatre. She uses magical rhymes and pictures made from pixie dust to weave her tales. She can make shimmering shapes appear with a wave of her hand.

Pirates, Ho!

In this thrilling show, the fairies tell the story of a pirate ship arriving in Never Land. Giant pirate figures made from pixie dust move all over the theatre and through the audience.

Type of Bug

Firefly

Favourite Game

Fetch

Names Tinker Bell Guesses for Him

Blinky, Flicker, Flash, Beam, Flare and Bellows

Blaze

With his huge green eyes, plump cheeks and squeaky voice, Blaze is adorable from his antennae down to his blinking bottom. Despite his cute nature, Blaze is spirited, fiery and full of bright ideas. No wonder he and Tinker Bell become such good friends!

The reflection from Blaze's glow lights Tink's way to treasure. Could the enchanted Mirror of Incanta be in there?

Adopt-a-Bug

When he is accidentally separated from his fellow fireflies, Blaze ends up on Tink's balloon and eats all the food for her journey to the Lost Island. Blaze wants to stay with Tink, but she isn't sure at first.

Calling All Bugs!

When her balloon crashes, Tink has no food, water or pixie dust. She is in big trouble! Blaze blinks a distress signal and soon hundreds of bug buddies rush to the rescue.

When Blaze is sad, his antennae droop.

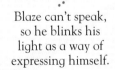

Fright Light

Blaze might only be a little firefly, but his light can create something terrifying! To frighten away some scary rats, Tink shines Blaze's light onto some spider webs to cast the shadow of a monster.

Blaze holds his two front legs up like a puppy begging for love.

Blaze can't speak, so he blinks his light as a way of expressing himself.

Fairy Lights

Fairies often ask fireflies to light their way in the dark or to add twinkle to their evening celebrations.

A Friend Indeed

Blaze not only helps light Tink's way on her adventure to the Lost Island. He also lights up her heart with some important lessons about friendship through his determined loyalty, bravery and forgiveness.

69

Never Land

Do you know the way to Never Land?
Just look to the night sky, find the second
star to the right and follow it until
morning. You'll discover a hidden world
filled with magic and adventure, where
fairies fly and legends come alive.

Due north of
Never Land is the
spooky Lost Island.
Tink sets out to find
it using her cotton-
puff balloon.

Indian Camp

The Lost Island
Never Land's north island is so
misty and dark, it's tough to tell a
stone archway from a twisted tree.
It's a good place to have a firefly
like Blaze for a friend!

The Shipwreck
This shadowy shipwreck on the
spooky island holds ancient
enchantments, lost treasures and
even a surprise or two! Would you
be brave enough to climb inside?

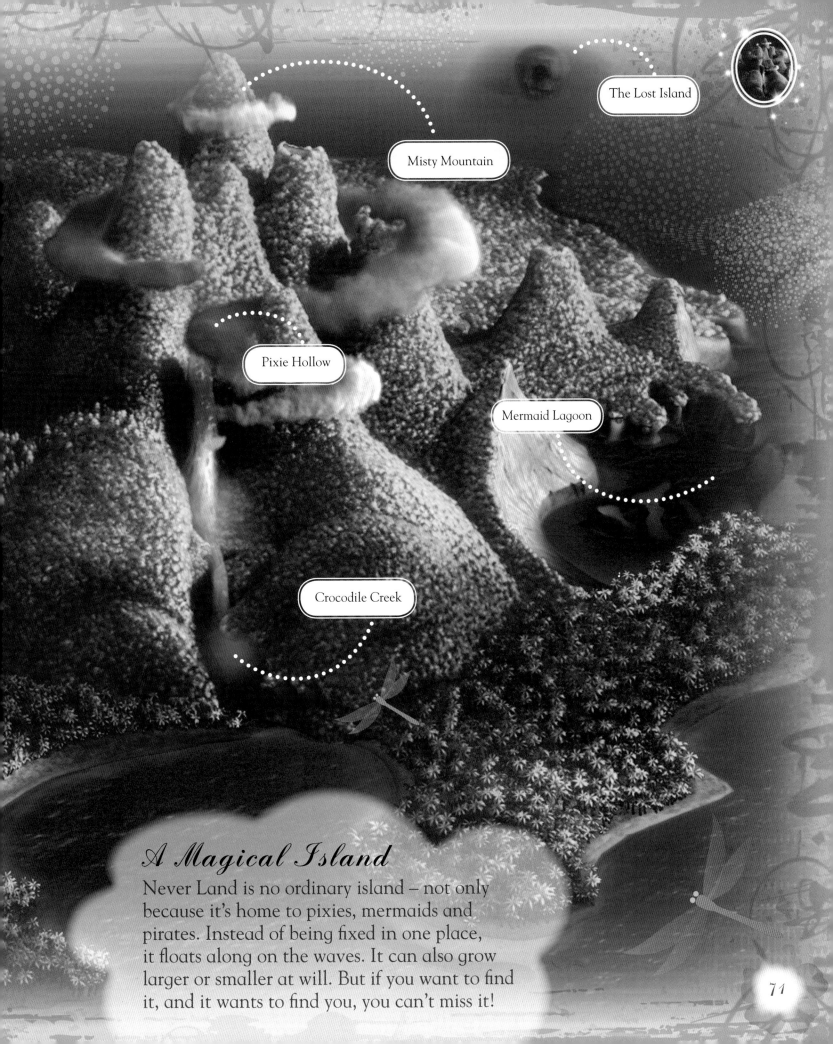

The Lost Island

Misty Mountain

Pixie Hollow

Mermaid Lagoon

Crocodile Creek

A Magical Island

Never Land is no ordinary island – not only
because it's home to pixies, mermaids and
pirates. Instead of being fixed in one place,
it floats along on the waves. It can also grow
larger or smaller at will. But if you want to find
it, and it wants to find you, you can't miss it!

71

Leech and Grimsley

By nature, trolls are dim-witted and as dull as logs, and these two are no exception! Leech is the short, lumpy one, while Grimsley is the tall, bumpy one. They love to insult each other, but they're not as thick-skinned as they look – deep down they are good friends, and they even teach Tinker Bell a thing or two about friendship!

Home
The Lost Island

Job
Guarding the secret bridge

Favourite Insults
Wart face, booger breath, garden gnome (Leech especially hates this one!)

Bickering and making up is the trolls' favourite hobby. What else is there to do to pass the time?

"My turn to give the ominous warning, blockhead!"

Troll Guardians

The bridge is a dark tunnel of twisted vines. The trolls have been guarding it for hundreds of years, but they have been there so long, they don't remember why!

Trespassers

Tinker Bell was surprised to see two trolls guarding the secret bridge – she thought it was a toll bridge! The big, ugly trolls should be terrifying, but Tink isn't afraid. She is crossing that bridge and no one can stop her!

72

Gruesome Twosome

With bulbous noses, broken teeth, bald heads, scaly legs and bodies covered with twisted roots, Leech and Grimsley are never going to win a beauty contest – unless it's held by trolls!

Say the Magic Words

Even though they argue, Leech and Grimsley are deep-rooted friends. When Grimsley makes Leech feel bad, he never forgets to apologise to his friend, and they help Tinker Bell to realise she has been mean to Terence.

Leech hates being so much smaller than Grimsley.

Trolls have only four fingers on each hand.

A troll's legs are so skinny and knobbly, it's a wonder that they can stand up on them!

The Lost Island

This place is not for the faint-hearted fairy! On her adventure to the Lost Island north of Never Land, Tinker Bell reaches a skull-shaped rock. Its shape warns any visitors that the island is just as sinister as it looks. In her little cotton-puff balloon, Tink carries on into the unknown in search of the Mirror of Incanta. Tink broke the fairies' sacred moonstone, and now she must fix it – she hopes the magical mirror can help!

One Wish

Tinker Bell has travelled over Never Land, across the old troll bridge and through Skull Rock to reach this legendary treasure: the Mirror of Incanta. The mirror can grant three wishes, but long ago, some pirates used up two of them. Tink wants to use the mirror's last wish to fix the fairies' sacred moonstone. But can this hot-headed fairy keep her cool and make the one wish that will mean the most?

"Blaze, I wish you'd be quiet for one minute!"

"I wish Terence were here.

I wish we were still friends."

77

Blue Moon

The blue moon rises only once every eight years, and when it does, the fairies are ready to catch its precious light. They make a special sceptre to hold a moonstone. When the blue moon's light passes through the sceptre, the light creates the powerful blue pixie dust that replenishes the Pixie Dust Tree.

Minister of Summer

With a laugh as warm as the season she loves, this jolly Minister of Summer almost never worries. It's a big job to bring summer to the Mainland, but her good humour and free spirit make preparing for the season a happy task!

Fawn and the nature-talent fairies paint each unique pair of butterfly wings.

Summer is Here!

Oh, I think summer is the most wonderful season – don't you? There's nothing so pleasant as a soft, warm breeze over a field of wildflowers or the croak of a happy frog cooling off in a rippling brook!

Garden fairies encourage summer blossoms to bloom all season.

Summer on the Mainland

With its long, lazy days, summer is unlike any other season. Fairies and humans alike slow down a little to enjoy the fragrant flowers and welcoming sunshine.

Animal fairies teach choirs of baby crickets how to sing.

Fairy Camp

All summer long, fairies stay on the Mainland to stir up warm breezes, ripen sweet fruits and paint stripes on bumblebees. Fairy camp is their home away from home, with all the comforts of Pixie Hollow hidden under one tree.

To the Mainland!

If you look up to the sky and see twinkles of light, it might just be fairies in flight! In summer, fairies fly to the Mainland and set up a secret fairy camp, where they live all season long. Fairies fly over with doves, who carry the pixies' possessions in tinker-made leaf baskets.

Fairy Foods

Just like humans, every fairy has a favourite snack or sweet treat that gives her wings an extra lift. With ingredients straight from the forest and fields, all of these snacks are fairy-fresh and so good to eat!

Fawn can't resist acorn butter – it makes everything delicious!

A Pixie Picnic

Sunny days are made for picnics with fairy friends. Beneath the trees, Bobble enjoys a small piece of bread while Clank happily munches a slice that's bigger than him!

Sweet Cheese

Cheese the mouse was named after his favourite food, but he can also be tempted by sweet treats like sugar cubes.

Tea for Two

A delicate set of cups and saucers from a doll's house is the perfect size for fairies – and makes any gathering extra-fancy!

What is Silvermist's favourite lunch? Water chestnuts, of course!

Today's Menu

Breakfast
Pumpkin muffins with acorn butter

Lunch
Dandelion greens with raspberry dressing

Snack
Sunflower-seed trail mix

Dinner
Boysenberry rolls with cheese

Dessert
Lemon tarts

Tinker Bell loves to eat a hearty breakfast of pumpkin muffins.

Berries from the garden and buttercup soup keep Rosetta's cheeks rosy.

Iridessa's sweet tooth craves golden-yellow lemon-meringue pie.

Age

8 years old

Favourite Pastime

Drawing pictures of
fairies – real or imaginary

Favourite Colour

Green, like
Tinker Bell!

Lizzy

Do you believe in fairies? Lizzy does!
She believes they're as real as she is,
and she wishes her father would
listen to her about it. When
this sweet, lonely girl meets
Tinker Bell, it's her
dream come true.

A busy scientist, Lizzy's
father has very little time for
her – and no patience for her
fairy "fantasies".

Busy Lizzy

Lizzy loves to spend
her time drawing
pictures of fairies
and building tiny
fairy homes. Her
inventive and
creative nature is a
lot like her friend
Tinker Bell's!

Dainty Dollhouse

Excited about having a
fairy guest, Lizzy shows
Tinker Bell around her
room. Tink is delighted
by Lizzy's dollhouse.
Everything in it is the
perfect size for a pixie!

First Meeting

Fairies aren't meant to talk to humans. Before Lizzy captured Tink, the two species had never met.

Perfect Understanding

Lizzy hears Tinker Bell's words as delicate bell chimes. Although they can't speak, Tink pantomimes to her. Tink even teaches Lizzy to fly – with help from a sprinkling of pixie dust, of course!

"You don't have to understand. You just have to believe it."

Lizzy keeps her hair tied back in braids so it doesn't get in the way when she is painting.

Lizzy's smile is friendly.

Dreamer

Lizzy needs her father's attention and she wants him to believe in her dreams. Thanks to Tinker Bell, Lizzy's father learns to listen to Lizzy, and the two grow closer than ever.

This pretty pinafore has a pocket for Lizzy's pencils and paintbrushes.

Dr Griffiths

Rational Dr Griffiths only believes in facts that can be seen or proven scientifically. He pays close attention to every detail of his work as a scientist – but he doesn't observe that his daughter Lizzy needs attention, too!

Job
Scientist

Home
London, and a country cottage in the summer months

Pet Peeves
Being disturbed, nonsense

Although he loves his daughter, Dr Griffiths puts his work first and never has much time for Lizzy.

Butterflies Beware!

The butterflies Dr Griffiths mounts and frames are all just scientific specimens to him. But Lizzy and Tinker Bell help him to see them as beautiful living creatures.

Make Believe
Dr Griffiths only believes what he sees. Fairies don't let humans see them, so he thinks they don't exist.

Dr Griffiths doesn't like to use his mind to imagine or dream.

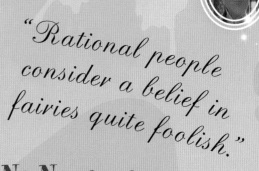

"Rational people consider a belief in fairies quite foolish."

No-Nonsense

Dr Griffiths has ambitions to be recognised by the British Museum for his work and he expects Lizzy to share his own enthusiasm for scientific thought. He loves Lizzy but thinks her love of fairies is nonsense – though he soon discovers otherwise!

Wears plainly coloured, serious-looking clothing.

Makes detailed drawings for his scientific journal.

Time to Believe!

It takes lots of pixie dust for Dr Griffiths to find his faith and trust, but when he does, he is ready to soar. Finally learning to have fun, he moves the hands of Big Ben – something he has always wanted to do!

Mr Twitches

Mr Twitches, the Griffiths' perpetually hungry cat, only believes in what he can eat! Thanks to Tink's friends and a lot of catnip, Mr Twitches now sees mice like Cheese as friends, not food.

bad bad news

89

The Mainland

Humans live on the Mainland, far from the world of the fairies, but it is here that fairies are at their most magical. They frost winter windows, wake sleeping animals in spring and spend all summer in a secret fairy camp as they help flowers bloom and bring nature to life!

Follow the second star, over the breeze and across the waves, to reach the Mainland.

Lighted windows give the city a magic all its own!

Family Cottage

Much of the Mainland is busy and bustling. But Dr Griffiths and his daughter, Lizzy, spend the summer at this quiet country cottage, just a stone's throw from fairy camp.

Fairies in the House!

Silvermist, Rosetta and Iridessa would never normally enter a human house. But with daring Tinker Bell around, nothing is ever quite normal!

A giant clock is a tinker's dream!

Dr Griffiths works in a big museum in London.

The Big City

In the city of London on the Mainland, towering buildings, shops and family homes are crowded together. It looks very different from Pixie Hollow, but to Tinker Bell it's "flitterific"!

Mainlanders go into this building to make important decisions.

Pixie Trail

Most Mainlanders don't notice, but those who really believe can find proof of fairies all around. If you are very lucky, you may even spot one flying past your window!

Lizzy's Fairy House

A great imagination doesn't need to see to believe! This miniature cottage is a perfect fit for fairy folk, even though Lizzy had never actually seen a fairy when she built it. From a charming walkway to a pair of fluffy pillows, every thoughtful detail welcomes passing fairies inside.

Leaf-covered roof lifts off to peek inside.

Fairies can even have their mail delivered here!

Fairy Mail

Dainty Decorations

The cosy bedroom has a fascinating geared clock on one wall, a table filled with fairy-size snacks and a comfy bed that's a perfect fit for fairies.

Dandelions look like puffs of smoke.

Pretty Play House

With its leaf roof and twig pillars, Lizzy's fairy house looks a bit like a real Pixie Hollow home. But look closely and you'll see the human touches – like cereal-box walls and glued-on beans on the chimney top!

Bell tinkles when the door moves.

Come On In!

Tink is amazed to find a fairy-size home near the human house. Adventurous Tink can't resist taking the chance to investigate something so exciting and new!

Cheerful blooms brighten the entryway.

Lizzy's Drawings

Lizzy's father, Dr Griffiths, insists that she studies real facts, just like he does with his butterfly research. So Lizzy does just that! She fills her sketchbook with fairy facts and drawings to show her father.

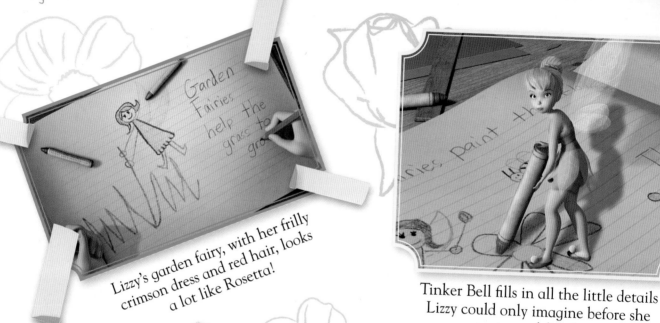

Lizzy's garden fairy, with her frilly crimson dress and red hair, looks a lot like Rosetta!

Tinker Bell fills in all the little details Lizzy could only imagine before she met a real-life fairy.

Lizzy's drawing shows how animal fairies help their furry friends.

Lizzy even draws the fairies' flight to the Mainland, over the human rooftops to bring in the seasons.

Tink teaches Lizzy about the jobs water fairies do and what they are like, right down to the colour of Silvermist's dress.

Lizzy includes directions to Never Land, starting with the second star to the right that you should follow.

Like a good scientist, Lizzy records the exact size of her subject.

A Pixie Hollow pop-up is so pretty, it makes Tink feel a little homesick for the fairy land.

A Scientific Study

Lizzy never doubted for a minute that fairies were real . . . but before she met Tinker Bell, she could only guess how they looked and lived. With Tink's help, her "scientific" book is now filled with all the fairy facts she needs!

Fairy Wear

Handy Tinker Bell makes her green outfits herself out of leaves and other natural materials. Each one is tailored to its use, but perfect for Tink: inventive, practical, comfortable and strong enough for any adventure!

Grass makes a perfect belt.

Cotton balls and pussy willows add the perfect cosy touch to winter clothes.

Green leaves give all of Tinker Bell's outfits their signature colour.

Winter Wear

Tink adds a fuzzy trim and extra layers to keep warm in the Winter Woods. The long, fitted sleeves keep out the cold air, the short cut of the coat means she can move easily and the boots are long enough for treading in snow.

A visored hat shields Tink from sun and rain.

This buttoned capelet adds warmth when needed but keeps arms free.

Tink's boots are made from leaves and tied together with vines.

Travel Wear

When setting out on an expedition, it is best to be prepared for anything! Tink wears long sleeves and trousers to keep her warm in the wind and practical accessories like a hat, a cape and sturdy boots fit for any terrain.

Top fits snugly, with no loose pieces to tangle in inventions.

Everyday Wear

Tinker Bell's regular outfit is short, simple and just right for a tinker, as it leaves her arms free for gathering lost things and tinkering. Believe it or not, this was once a tunic big enough to fit Clank – but Tink adapted it to fit her perfectly!

Tink's tiny shoes are topped with dandelion fluff from her arrival outfit.

Custom-made Clothes

Tinker Bell makes a pattern to see how all the pieces of her outfit will fit together. It's a little like building a tinker machine or invention!

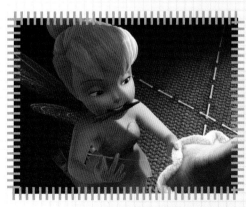

A thorn needle and thread keep a furry lining in place. It's pretty and also very warm – perfect for cold-weather adventures.

Tink loves to explore, so she hammers hard-wearing soles onto her boots to make them strong.

Wild Friends

Tinker Bell and her friends are close to all the birds, bugs and animals around Pixie Hollow. The fairies help the wild creatures, who in turn help the fairies, too. It's all about sharing and enjoying the beauty of nature together.

Crickets

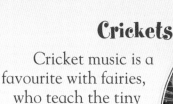

Cricket music is a favourite with fairies, who teach the tiny creatures to chirp. Crickets perform in the orchestra at the fairy theatre, and they also make great alarm clocks!

Bunnies

Fairies comb stickers and burrs from bunnies' fluffy tails, and bunnies give the fairies their fluff to make cosy blankets or slippers.

Snowy Owls

These strong and beautiful creatures fly from the Winter Woods to Tinkers' Nook to pick up snowflake baskets for the winter fairies to use.

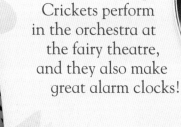

Pill Bugs

Even the tiniest creatures can be a very big help! When Tink loses her way on her adventure to the Lost Island, tiny pill bugs bring her morsels of food to eat and drops of dew to drink.

Bug Clock

A buzzing beetle has a job as a clock at the Pixie Dust Depot. When the beetle buzzes, dust-keeper fairies know it's time to start or stop their work.

Spiders

The fairies decorate spiders' webs with gleaming drops of dew, while the fairies' finest fabrics are made from spider silk.

98

Bluebirds

Animal fairies like Fawn teach baby bluebirds to fly. The sweet-voiced birds repay the fairies' kindness with a special gift of their own – the gift of song at every fairy occasion.

Butterfly Babies

To make sure butterflies hatch with strong wings that are ready for flight, the fairies care for butterfly chrysalises, keeping them warm and dry.

Tadpoles

Silvermist and other water-talent fairies love teaching bouncy baby tadpoles how to blow bubbles through rings for special occasions like the Autumn Revelry.

Doves

Doves are among the fairies' most valuable helpers. They can fly great distances so they carry baskets of supplies to the Mainland to help the fairies bring in each new season.

Marmots

Marmots are helpful fairy lookouts because they whistle to warn of danger. The fairies comb them for fur to make waterproof capes for themselves, and they also help the marmots travel across to the Winter Woods in time to hibernate there.

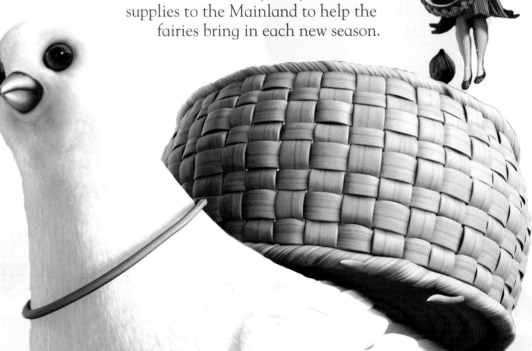

Fly With Me!

Have you ever wondered what it would be like to go on a fairy adventure? Well, now you can do more than just wonder. Come along with Tinker Bell and find out what it's like to be a pixie on the go!

Where to, fairies?

The Winter Woods

Would you like an animal travel companion?

yes

no

Through the snow or through the clouds?

Downhill or up high?

Snow

Dewey's lynx, Fiona, bounds through the snow faster than anyone!

Clouds

You can see all of the Winter Woods from up here! Snowy owls are great for tinker deliveries, too.

Catch a drift

Take a ride with the winter fairies. What a rush!

Catch a snowflake

Cold-weather fairies can fly through the heaviest snow.

The Mainland

Got deliveries to make?

Pixie Hollow

Got a lot to carry?

no

Follow the path or catch the breeze?

no

How's the weather?

yes

yes

Rain

Protect your wings with a leaf or paper umbrella.

Sunny

Hooray for sunny days! Join your fairy friends and fly up high.

Grab a ride

Hop on! Cheese can take us anywhere Pixie Hollow's roads go.

Spread your wings

There's nothing like your first view of Pixie Hollow from the sky!

Water

There's plenty of room on a boat. Raise a sail, catch the wind and off we go!

Water, land or air?

Load a cart

Count on Cheese to help! His cart carries deliveries to fairies all over Pixie Hollow.

Cart, boat or balloon?

Up, up and away!

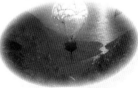

With tinker-thinking and some pixie dust, we can float through the clouds in a balloon.

Land

Hide away on a human invention. How does this thing work, anyway?

Air

Doves are super-strong – we can fill this basket and bring along all our favourite things from Pixie Hollow!

Take a cruise

Riding on a pixie-made boat is always an adventure. Hold onto your pixie dust!

Blankets of snow are rolled up in the Winter Woods, then spread out on the Mainland.

Winter Wonderland

The fairies work all year round to make enough frost, snow and ice for the Mainland. When their work is done, the result is truly magical!

When animals migrate from the Autumn Woods to the Winter Woods, their coats turn white.

Snowflakes are delivered to the Mainland in baskets made by tinker fairies in Tinkers' Nook.

Frost fairies coat branches – and windows on the Mainland – with delicate snow and ice crystals.

This no-nonsense minister is a great scholar of snow and sees to winter preparations with icy precision. Her elegant look requires no fuss – just an ice-water rinse to keep her hair shiny!

WOW!

Introducing Winter

Bundle up and come along into winter. There is much to discover! Look closely and you'll see a variety of snowflakes – there are many types, according to my studies. We've discovered several categories of icicle, too, and we're only just breaking the ice.

The Divide

A stream separates the Winter Woods from the rest of Pixie Hollow. Animals cross it by walking over bridges or flying overhead, but warm-season fairies are forbidden to go to the other side.

The woods look dark and mysterious

The Winter Woods

This frozen realm covered with snow and ice is so cold, only winter fairies can fly here. The rules here for warm-weather fairies like Tinker Bell and her friends are very strict: do not enter! If they do, the cold weather could damage their fragile wings.

Snowy owls fly between the Winter Woods and the rest of Pixie Hollow to make deliveries. These snowflake baskets were made in Tinkers' Nook.

Beautifully
frosted branches

Year-round snow

Winter Sports

In the Winter Woods, winter
fairies skim across ice as
naturally as walking. For
warm-weather fairies like Tink,
ice-skating takes practise ... and
a pair of lost things for skates!

Frosted Splendour

Frost fairies transform a stark forest into a
shimmering spectacle. Each branch and bristle
takes on the beauty of a crystal
at the fairies' icy touch.

Lord Milori

Imposing and intense, Lord Milori watches over the Winter Woods like a firm but loving father. He believes he knows what is best for his fairy subjects, and they always respect his decisions. Only his old friend Dewey would ever argue back!

Role
Rules the Winter Woods

Trusty Transport
A snowy owl wearing a jewelled necklace

Pet Peeve
When Dewey breaks the rules

Lord Milori has a broken wing, so he flies on a snowy owl to keep watch over the Winter Woods.

Winter Watchman

Lord Milori notices everything. When he discovers the *Wingology* book in the Winter Woods, he knows it is from the warm seasons of Pixie Hollow and is concerned that a warm-weather fairy might be in his realm.

Loving Leader

Lord Milori is a kind leader and he cares about his winter fairies' welfare. He abides by rules to protect his subjects – especially the rule that forbids them from crossing into Pixie Hollow.

Silver hair is the colour of moonlight on snow.

Serious Role

Lord Milori keeps firm control over his emotions and never lets them show. This can sometimes seem intimidating, but he just takes his responsibility for the safety of all his charges very seriously.

Broken Wings

There is no cure for a broken fairy wing. If a fairy's wing is damaged, they can never fly again.

High leaf boots are good for walking in snowdrifts.

A cape of snowy owl feathers covers his broken wing.

Secret Love

The decision to keep the Winter Woods and the rest of Pixie Hollow separate has parted Lord Milori and Queen Clarion, but their love lives on.

A nurse asks patients questions to help the doctor figure out what is wrong.

Fairy Urgent Care

Even light-as-air pixies can sometimes land with a thump! When things go wrong – like crashing into rainbows, getting stuck inside a flower or getting tangled up in a toad's tongue – fairies and sparrow men head to Fairy Urgent Care.

Patient #1: an animal fairy

Book about pixie ailments

Exam toadstool

Patient #2: a tongue-tied toad

Another Tricky Case

Healing-talent fairies are the doctors, nurses and receptionists who run Fairy Urgent Care. There are various examination rooms that deal with all kinds of unusual cases, but the job is always the same: figure out the problem, then make it all better!

Clinic Reception

At the Fairy Urgent Care reception desk, the injured fairy (or her worried friends!) gives her name to the fairy receptionist, then she takes a seat inside the waiting room.

Exam Lights

Special lampshades help focus firefly light on the patient. Shining the brightest lights helps the doctors and nurses see the patient's problem clearly.

Medicinal plant

A Closer Look

Some issues (like getting wedged inside a snapdragon) are easy to diagnose. But for rarer cases, a magnifying glass helps the healing-talent fairies examine every little detail.

109

Dewey

Role

The Keeper of All Fairy Knowledge

Home

The Hall of Winter in the Winter Woods

Pet

Fiona the snow lynx

Meet the Keeper of All Fairy Knowledge, or Dewey to his closest friends! As the Keeper, Dewey collects all fairy lore and writes it down in books. Everyone in Pixie Hollow and the Winter Woods respects and reveres him.

In a grand ice cavern, Dewey etches fairy wisdom and history onto frozen ice books.

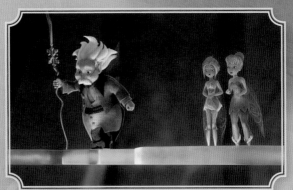

Solving the Mystery

With his knowledge of fairy lore, Dewey helps Tink and Periwinkle discover the truth about their mysterious sparkling wings. He even breaks the rules to give them time together in the Winter Woods.

Old Friends

Lord Milori is one of the few people who calls the Keeper by his first name! The two are old friends, and Dewey often acts as Lord Milori's confidante. Dewey is the only fairy bold enough to question Milori's decisions.

The Sparkling

"The sparkling" is very rare. Wings only sparkle when two fairies borne of the same laugh meet.

"I've never seen the sparkling with my own peepers till now."

Behind Dewey's thick glasses, his blue eyes have a twinkle of fun in them.

A soft leaf suit and waistcoat keep Dewey comfortable in the ice cavern where he works.

Kooky Keeper

With his furry eyebrows, rebellious hair and habit of talking to himself, Dewey may seem a little kooky, but he is incredibly knowledgeable. Dewey knows every fact on every page of every book he ever wrote!

Small Wings

Dewey was born with small wings, so he sometimes uses a long cane instead of his wings to hover in the air. When Dewey needs to travel quickly, he rides his pet snow lynx, Fiona, who lives with him in the Hall of Winter.

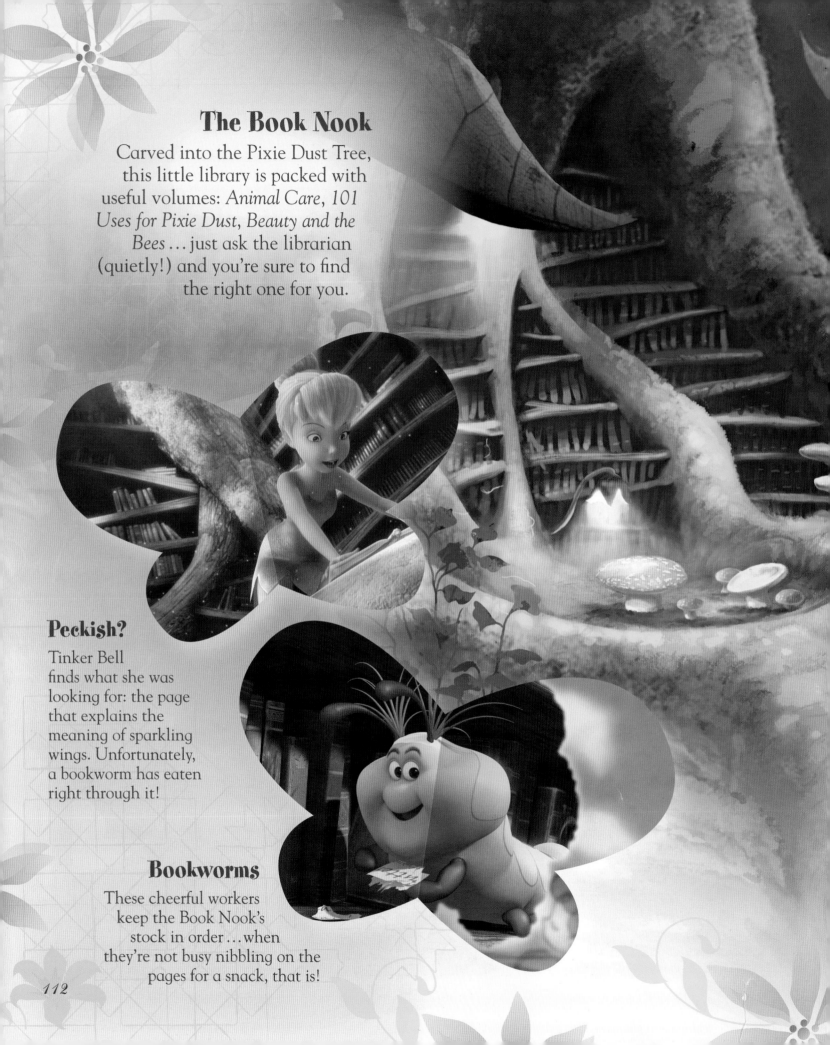

The Book Nook

Carved into the Pixie Dust Tree, this little library is packed with useful volumes: *Animal Care, 101 Uses for Pixie Dust, Beauty and the Bees*... just ask the librarian (quietly!) and you're sure to find the right one for you.

Peckish?

Tinker Bell finds what she was looking for: the page that explains the meaning of sparkling wings. Unfortunately, a bookworm has eaten right through it!

Bookworms

These cheerful workers keep the Book Nook's stock in order... when they're not busy nibbling on the pages for a snack, that is!

Sparkling wing
When a
, most
incredible
the sparkl
ere were tw
just makes it
for fairies
When a
s wings are
ith just one
PixieD

Light Reading

Wingology, written by Dewey, is too good to put down – but if you try, it may fly away! This book has wings and it's all about wings: care and keeping, flapping and fluttering . . . Now where's that page about sparkling?

This well-read fairy keeps a careful eye on the books . . . and an ear open for any troublesome noisemakers!

Wingology

So you say you would like to know about wings? Well of course, there are many fascinating books here in the Book Nook, but you'll find what you need in *Wingology*. Don't mind the bookworm. And please do be quiet!

The Bodc of The Never Beast

Hall of Winter

Everything there is to know about fairy history can be found in this frosty library. It is here that Dewey, the Keeper of All Fairy Knowledge, etches every fairy fact onto ice books. But as part of the winter realm, the Hall of Winter is forbidden to warm-weather fairies.

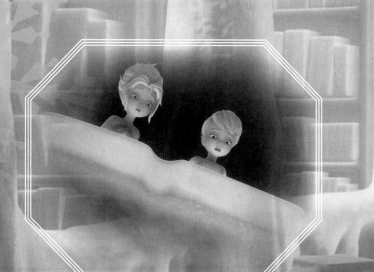

The books here are actually tablets of ice.

Mysteries to Light

When Tink and the winter fairy Periwinkle are near each other, their wings sparkle. In the Great Hall, Dewey directs the two fairies to stand on a big snowflake, which rises up into a ray of sunlight. When light passes through the fairies' wings, images from the past are projected on the icy walls.

Most of these stacks of ice books are taller than Dewey!

Lord Milori would not be happy if he knew a warm-weather fairy was hiding here!

Enter via a large ice door – unless you're a warm-weather fairy!

There are rows of books on shelves of ice.

The Dewey System

Could you find the ice book you need in these towering stacks? Dewey can! He wrote every one of them himself, and he remembers what is on every single page – even the ones that are missing!

One Laugh

Dewey shows Tink and Peri the story of their history on giant columns of ice: they were borne of the same baby's laugh – which makes them fairy sisters!

Talent
Frost fairy

Home
The Winter
Woods

Dreams of . . .
Seeing summer, butterflies,
and the Pixie
Dust Tree

Periwinkle

Graceful as a snowflake, this frost fairy is always cool and perfectly poised. Peri loves the winter world she lives in, but has always been drawn to the forbidden world outside it – and now she knows why! Borne from the same laugh but separated at birth, Periwinkle is Tink's sister.

Both Tink's and Periwinkle's wings sparkle when they come near each other – something that surprises and intrigues them both.

Frosty Fun

Now that they have found each other, Peri and Tink are inseparable. Peri shows Tink her winter world and her favourite way to spend her downtime – a toboggan ride down a frozen waterfall!

Shy Side

Periwinkle is curious, perky and friendly like Tinker Bell, but she is a little more timid than her feisty sister. Peri isn't sure there is any way they can be together, but Tink is determined to change the rules!

"I'm a frost fairy. I frost things."

Periwinkle's ice-white hair is like a swirl of frost.

Peri is comfortable in the cold, so her sleeveless tunic is warm enough.

Wing Twins

Fairy wings are usually all different. Identical wings like Tink's and Peri's are extremely rare.

Secret Sister

When they meet, the sisters have an instant connection – but neither of them could have guessed why. Now Peri knows she has a sister in Pixie Hollow, she is even more desperate to travel outside the Winter Woods.

Touring Tink's World

Periwinkle burns with curiosity about all the different seasons and pores over ice books about them. Thanks to her inventive sister's snow-making machine, Peri can tour the magical warm-weather world without worrying that her winter wings will wilt!

Wears cute pompoms on her shoes, just like Tinker Bell.

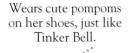

117

Talent

Frost fairy

Special Skill

Delicate dancing

Favourite Thing

Autumn acorns – even though she's never seen one!

"Bring me back an acorn . . . a big one!"

Gliss

Like her best friends Periwinkle and Spike, Gliss is a frost fairy, and she adores what she does. She dances over leaves and plants with a light touch, spinning frost as artistic and as fine as lace.

Positive Pixie

Gliss gets along with everyone she meets. Her enthusiastic, upbeat personality makes the pixie a positive pleasure to be around!

Slender leaf leggings give flexibility for fast frost-painting moves.

Warm Welcome

When Gliss discovers Peri has a sister, she couldn't be happier for her best friend. The warm-hearted pixie gives Tinker Bell a warm welcome to the Winter Woods.

Pointy-toed shoes make delicate frost patterns on leaves and plants.

Silver belt is fastened with sparkling ice crystal beads.

Feathers add a fluttery touch for when Spike is working at speed.

Spike

Athletic, powerful and fast, Spike is a talented frost fairy – but she is too cool to get all geeky about it! Spike has a frosty temperament that fits her job description perfectly, but she is always there for her friends.

Talent
Frost fairy

Special Skill
Lightning-fast speed

Dislikes
Getting all geeked up about things

"For the record, we shouldn't be doing this ...whatever it is we're doing."

Frost Friends

Spike and Peri are so different, it's surprising they're such good friends! Peri knows that beneath Spike's spiky sense of humour, the cynical sprite cares deeply for her friends.

Too Cool

Spike is a "frost ninja", with amazing strength and frosting skills. Though she pretends not to care about her talents, under her icy exterior Spike is really proud of them.

Talent
Winter animal-talent
fairy

Favourite Sport
Owl-racing

Pet Peeve
A lot of chatter

Sled

One cool dude, Sled is an animal-talent sparrow man who wrangles snowy owls. Like a cowboy with wings, Sled is the strong, silent type. He doesn't talk about his feelings – he just gets the job done.

Sleeveless leaf tunic keeps Sled's arms free for wrangling

"You'll be fine!"

Love in the Air

When their two worlds meet, Sled and Rosetta set eyes on each other and sparks fly. The big, strong sparrow man leaves Rosetta a little lost for words – a first for her!

Owl Whisperer

Sled raises, trains and rides snowy owls, and he has a great way with them. To Sled, the owls aren't just birds with a job to do – they're his friends.

Much too relaxed to worry about his hair, Sled just throws on his hat.

Slush

Laid-back Slush is probably the most relaxed fairy in the Winter Woods! He might have picked up his slow-moving, chilled-out attitude from the glaciers he tends to in his work.

"Yeah, now you've feelin' it, man!"

Job
Glacier-talent fairy

Favourite Pastime
Chatting with "Rooty", a root from the Pixie Dust Tree

Pet Peeve
Being rushed

Move Along

Slush is always glad to put the power of his thoughts to work. As his friends move an ice block for Tink's snow-making machine, Slush sends it some strong "moving" vibes.

Easy-going Guy

Slush may seem a little "out there" sometimes, but everyone in the Winter Woods accepts and likes him. Not much bothers Slush, which makes him very easy to be around.

Frosty Hollow

Warm-weather fairies take cover! When Tinker Bell's snow-making machine misfires, it churns out a blizzard. It's up to the winter fairies to save the Pixie Dust Tree and its precious pixie dust – without it, life in all of Pixie Hollow would be changed forever.

Fairies Unite

What a wintry celebration! All of Pixie Hollow is united once again and the warm-weather fairies experience the glittering beauty of the Winter Woods for the first time. Snowy owls drop snowflakes and periwinkles from the sky to mark the special moment. Most wonderful of all is enjoying the sight together with new friends!

Sisters

With their rare matching wings, Tink and Peri have always had a special connection, even when they were far apart. With their two worlds now joined, they can truly be together!

Warm-weather wings become white with a thin layer of frost.

Bundled Up

Warm-weather fairies wear extra layers to keep their bodies warm in the winter realm. Most importantly, the fairies have learned that a light coating of frost can protect their delicate wings from the cold.

Long-lost Love

Long ago, Queen Clarion and Lord Milori were in love, but they decided it was too dangerous to cross into each other's realms and said a sad farewell. No one is happier than them that their worlds are now united once again!

Fuzz-trimmed hats and coats keep out cold winter air.

Cold-weather fairies don't need to be bundled up! They are comfy in light clothing.

Goodbye from the Fairies

Every day is an adventure for a fairy – especially for one as fun-loving as Tinker Bell! Now you know how to spot a fairy, where fairies live and what they do, you could enjoy your own flitterific fairy adventure, too. All you have to do is believe…